For Rosie-jo, Scrumpy and Ben.
N.P.

First published in the United Kingdom in 2002
by David Bennett Books Limited,
64 Brewery Road, London N7 9NT.

A member of **Chrysalis** Books plc

BRITISH LIBRARY CATALOGUING-IN-PUBLICATION DATA
A catalogue record for this book is available from the British Library.

ISBN 1 85602 455 5
Printed in Hong Kong

The River

Nik Pollard

David Bennett Books

Way up high,
clouds scud by.

Raindrops
drip,
drip, drop.

Wind whistles,
a stream trickles,

a hiker hopes
the rain will
stop.

Ravens caw **caw** **caw**
as they **soar**
above the stream.

The water
babbles, bubbles, gurgles, gushes
around the rocks

and through the rushes.

Cows slurp,
mud spurts,
as wheels turn
and churn.

The truck makes **splashes**
as it **dashes** across
the widening stream.

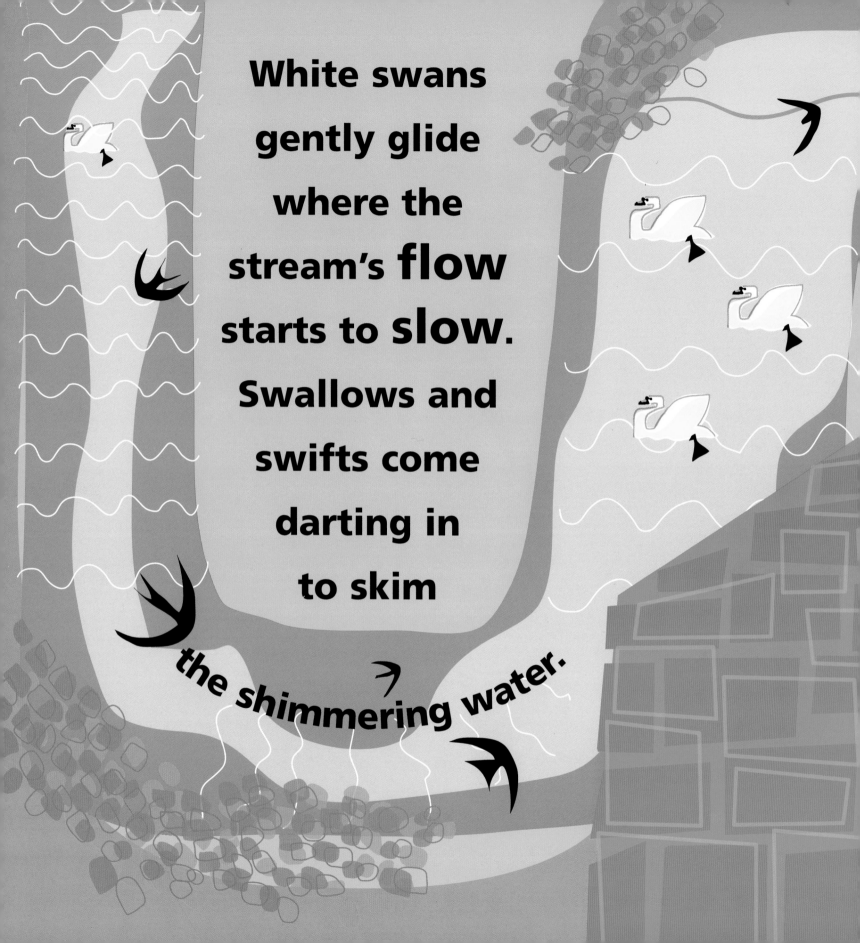

White swans
gently glide
where the
stream's **flow**
starts to **slow.**
Swallows and
swifts come
darting in
to skim

the shimmering water.

In the stream's safe shallows, where a willow spreads its shadow...

children catch **minnows!**

The stream flows down to the town.

Now it is wider.
Now it is **bigger.**

Now it's a river.

The river sweeps
into open spaces...

...where
splashing,
dashing canoes amuse
the crowds watching the races.

Water laps with soft slop-slaps.

Hush!

A pike.
It lurks
in green
weed...
unseen.

A fisherman drops his bait into the whorls and swirls... and waits.

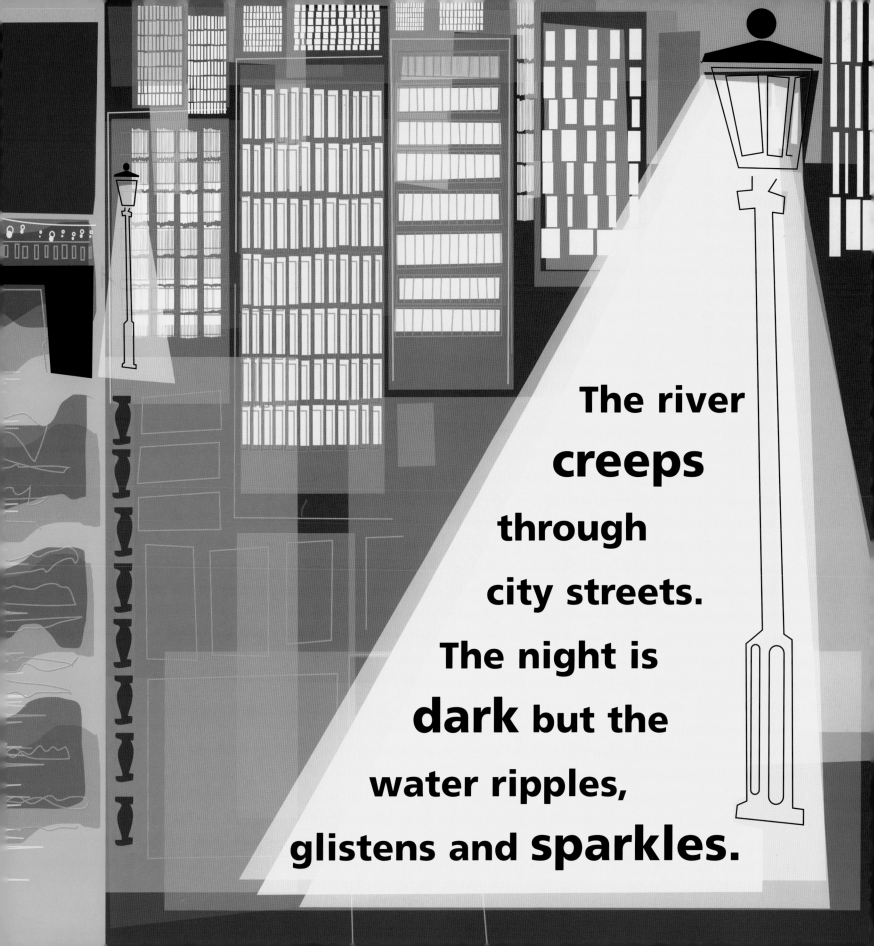

The river **creeps** through city streets. The night is **dark** but the water ripples, glistens and **sparkles.**

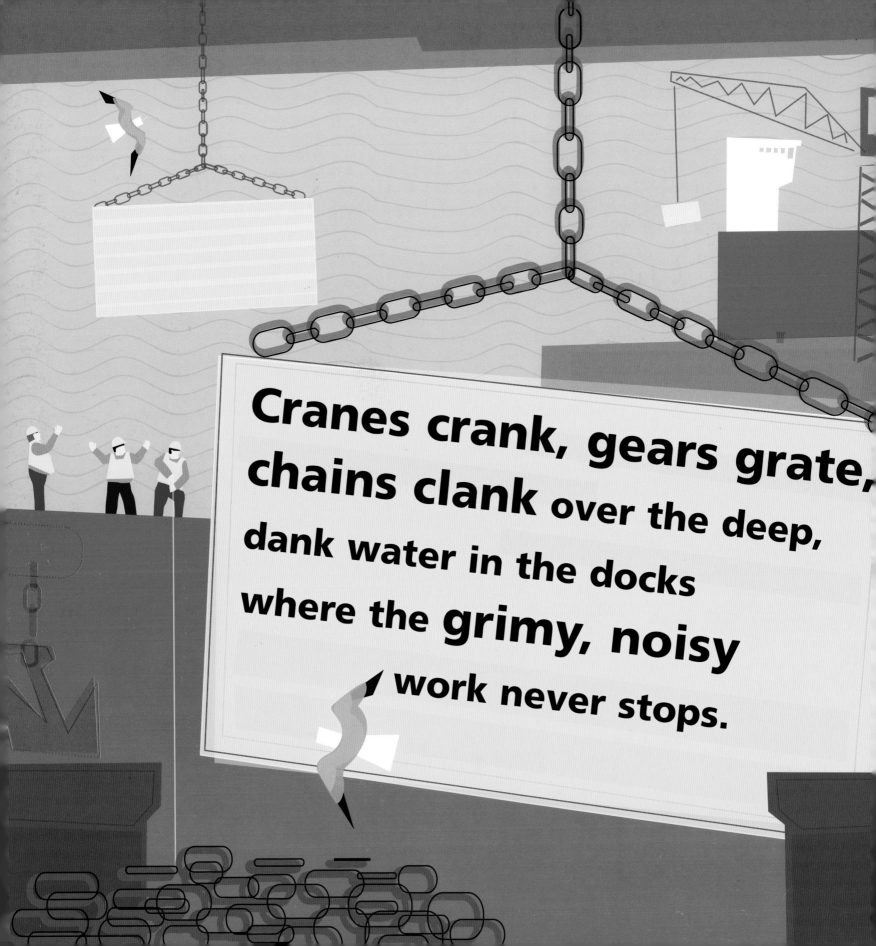

A **big ship** starts its journey as the river nears its end.

Horns sound

and little boats

bob around...

where the river meets the sea.